THE PHANTOM OF THE OPERA

Do you believe in ghosts? Of course not. We like to talk about ghosts, and to tell stories about them, but we don't really believe in them . . . do we?

In the Paris Opera House in 1880, strange things are happening. One of the dancers sees a shadow in a dark passage. It comes through a wall in front of her, and its face has no eyes. One of the stage workers sees a man in a black evening coat, but he has the head of a dead man, with a yellow face and no nose. People hear a voice in another room, but the room is empty.

It is the Phantom of the Opera . . .

OXFORD BOOKWORMS LIBRARY
Fantasy & Horror

The Phantom of the Opera

Stage 1 (400 headwords)

Series Editor: Jennifer Bassett
Founder Editor: Tricia Hedge
Activities Editors: Jennifer Bassett and Alison Baxter

For
Richard

JENNIFER BASSETT

The Phantom
of the Opera

OXFORD UNIVERSITY PRESS

OXFORD
UNIVERSITY PRESS

Great Clarendon Street, Oxford, OX2 6DP, United Kingdom

Oxford University Press is a department of the University of Oxford.
It furthers the University's objective of excellence in research, scholarship,
and education by publishing worldwide. Oxford is a registered trade
mark of Oxford University Press in the UK and in certain other countries

ISBN: 978 0 19 478915 8   Book
ISBN: 978 0 19 462034 5   Book and audio pack

Printed in China

Word count (main text): 6,230 words

For more information on the Oxford Bookworms Library,
visit www.oup.com/elt/gradedreaders

ACKNOWLEDGEMENTS

Text adapted by Jennifer Bassett from the original by Gaston Leroux

Illustrated by Martin Cottam

Cover image by Bruno Passigatti courtesy of Shutterstock

The publisher would like to thank the following for permission to reproduce photographs:
Alamy p. 1 (KGPA Ltd).

CONTENTS

THE OPERA HOUSE IN PARIS is a very famous and beautiful building. It is the biggest Opera House in the world. Work on the building began in 1861, finished in 1875, and cost forty-seven million francs.

It has seventeen floors, ten above the ground, and seven under the ground. Behind and under the stage, there are stairs and passages and many, many rooms – dressing-rooms for the singers and the dancers, rooms for the stage workers, the opera dresses and shoes . . . There are more than 2,500 doors in the building. You can walk for hours and never see daylight, under the Paris Opera House.

And the Opera House has a ghost, a phantom, a man in black clothes. He is a body without a head, or a head without a body. He has a yellow face, he has no nose, he has black holes for eyes . . .

This is the true story of the Phantom of the Opera. It begins one day in 1880, in the dancers' dressing-room . . .

1

The dancers

'Quick! Quick! Close the door! It's him!' Annie Sorelli ran into the dressing-room, her face white.

One of the girls ran and closed the door, and then they all turned to Annie Sorelli.

'Who? Where? What's the matter?' they cried.

'It's the ghost!' Annie said. 'In the passage. I saw him. He came through the wall in front of me! And . . . and I saw his face!'

Most of the girls were afraid, but one of them, a tall girl with black hair, laughed.

'Pooh!' she said. 'Everybody says they see the Opera ghost, but there isn't really a ghost. You saw a shadow on the wall.' But she did not open the door, or look into the passage.

'Lots of people see him,' a second girl said. 'Joseph Buquet saw him two days ago. Don't you remember?'

Then all the girls began to talk at once.

'Joseph says the ghost is tall and he wears a black evening coat.'

'He has the head of a dead man, with a yellow face and no nose . . .'

' . . . And no eyes – only black holes!'

Then little Meg Giry spoke for the first time. 'Don't talk about him. He doesn't like it. My mother told me.'

'Your mother?' the girl with black hair said. 'What does your mother know about the ghost?'

'*Joseph says the ghost is tall and he wears a black evening coat.*'

'She says that Joseph Buquet is a fool. The ghost doesn't like people talking about him, and one day Joseph Buquet is going to be sorry, very sorry.'

'But what does your mother know? Tell us, tell us!' all the girls cried.

'Oh dear!' said Meg. 'But please don't say a word to anyone. You know my mother is the doorkeeper for some of the boxes in the Opera House. Well, Box 5 is the ghost's box! He watches the operas from that box, and sometimes he leaves flowers for my mother!'

'The ghost has a box! And leaves flowers in it!'

'Oh, Meg, your mother's telling you stories! How can the ghost have a box?'

'It's true, it's true, I tell you!' Meg said. 'Nobody buys tickets for Box 5, but the ghost always comes to it on opera nights.'

'So somebody does come there?'

'Why, no! . . . The ghost comes, but there is nobody there.'

The dancers looked at Meg. 'But how does your mother know?' one of them asked.

'There's no man in a black evening coat, with a yellow face. That's all wrong. My mother never sees the ghost in Box 5, but she hears him! He talks to her, but there is nobody there! And he doesn't like people talking about him!'

But that evening the dancers could not stop talking about the Opera ghost. They talked before the opera, all through the opera, and after the opera. But they talked very quietly, and they looked behind them before they spoke.

When the opera finished, the girls went back to their

dressing-room. Suddenly, they heard somebody in the passage, and Madame Giry, Meg's mother, ran into the room. She was a fat, motherly woman, with a red, happy face. But tonight her face was white.

'Oh girls,' she cried. 'Joseph Buquet is dead! You know he works a long way down, on the fourth floor under the stage. The other stage workers found his dead body there an hour ago – with a rope around his neck!'

'It's the ghost!' cried Meg Giry. 'The ghost killed him!'

2
The directors of the Opera House

The Opera House was famous, and the directors of the Opera House were very important men. It was the first week of work for the two new directors, Monsieur Armand Moncharmin and Monsieur Firmin Richard. In the directors' office the next day, the two men talked about Joseph Buquet.

'It was an accident,' Monsieur Armand said angrily. 'Or Buquet killed himself.'

'An accident? . . . Killed himself?' Monsieur Firmin said. 'Which story do you want, my friend? Or do you want the story of the ghost?'

'Don't talk to me about ghosts!' Monsieur Armand said. 'We have 1,500 people working for us in this Opera House, and everybody is talking about the ghost. They're all mad! I don't want to hear about the ghost, OK?'

Monsieur Firmin looked at a letter on the table next to him. 'And what are we going to do about this letter, Armand?'

'Do?' cried Monsieur Armand. 'Why, do nothing, of course! What can we do?'

The two men read the letter again. It wasn't very long.

To the new directors

Because you are new in the Opera House, I am writing to tell you some important things. Never sell tickets for Box 5; that is my box for every opera night. Madame Giry, the doorkeeper, knows all about it. Also, I need money for my work in the Opera House. I am not expensive, and I am happy to take only 20,000 francs a month. That is all. But please remember, I can be a good friend, but a bad enemy.

O.G.

'Don't sell tickets for Box 5! 20,000 francs a month!' Monsieur Armand was very angry again. 'That's the best box in the Opera House, and we need the money, Firmin! And who is this O.G., eh? Tell me that!'

'Opera ghost, of course,' Monsieur Firmin said. 'But you're right, Armand. We can do nothing about this letter. It's a joke, a bad joke. Somebody thinks we are fools, because we are new here. There are no ghosts in the Opera House!'

The two men then talked about the opera for that night. It was *Faust*, and usually La Carlotta sang Margarita. La Carlotta was Spanish, and the best singer in Paris. But today, La Carlotta was ill.

'Somebody thinks we are fools, because we are new here,'
Monsieur Firmin said.

'Everybody in Paris is going to be at the opera tonight,' said Monsieur Armand, 'and our best singer is ill. Suddenly! She writes a letter to us just this morning – she is ill, she cannot sing tonight!'

'Don't get angry again, Armand,' Monsieur Firmin said quickly. 'We have Christine Daaé, that young singer from Norway. She can sing Margarita tonight. She has a good voice.'

'But she's so young, and nobody knows her! Nobody wants to listen to a new singer.'

'Wait and see. Perhaps Daaé can sing better than La Carlotta. Who knows?'

3

Christine Daaé

Monsieur Firmin was right. All Paris talked about the new Margarita in *Faust*, the girl with the beautiful voice, the girl with the voice of an angel. People loved her. They laughed and cried and called for more. Daaé was wonderful, the best singer in the world!

Behind the stage Meg Giry looked at Annie Sorelli. 'Christine Daaé never sang like that before,' she said to Annie. 'Why was she so good tonight?'

'Perhaps she's got a new music teacher,' Annie said.

The noise in the Opera House went on for a long time. In Box 14, Philippe, the Comte de Chagny, turned to his younger brother and smiled.

'Well, Raoul, what did you think of Daaé tonight?'

Raoul, the Vicomte de Chagny, was twenty-one years old. He had blue eyes and black hair, and a wonderful smile. The Chagny family was old and rich, and many girls in Paris were in love with the young Vicomte. But Raoul was not interested in them.

He smiled back at his brother. 'What can I say? Christine is an angel, that's all. I'm going to her dressing-room to see her tonight.'

Philippe laughed. He was twenty years older than Raoul, and was more like a father than a brother.

'Ah, I understand,' he said. 'You are in love! But this is your

Daaé was wonderful, the best singer in the world!

first night in Paris, your first visit to the opera. How do you know Christine Daaé?'

'You remember four years ago, when I was on holiday by the sea, in Brittany?' Raoul said. 'Well, I met Christine there. I was in love with her then, and I'm still in love with her today!'

The Comte de Chagny looked at his brother. 'Mmm, I see,' he said slowly. 'Well, Raoul, remember she is only an opera singer. We know nothing about her family.'

But Raoul did not listen. To him, good families were not important, and young men never listen to their older brothers.

There were many people in Christine Daaé's dressing-room that night. But there was a doctor with Christine, and her beautiful face looked white and ill. Raoul went quickly across the room and took her hand.

'Christine! What's the matter? Are you ill?' He went down on the floor by her chair. 'Don't you remember me – Raoul de Chagny, in Brittany?'

Christine looked at him, and her blue eyes were afraid. She took her hand away. 'No, I don't know you. Please go away. I'm not well.'

Raoul stood up, his face red. Before he could speak, the doctor said quickly, 'Yes, yes, please go away. Everybody, please leave the room. Mademoiselle Daaé needs to be quiet. She is very tired.'

He moved to the door, and soon everybody left the room. Christine Daaé was alone in her dressing-room.

Outside in the passage the young Vicomte was angry and unhappy. How could Christine forget him? How could she say

that to him? He waited for some minutes, then, very quietly
and carefully, he went back to the door of her dressing-room.
But he did not open the door, because just then he heard *a
man's voice* in the room!

'Christine, you must love me!' the voice said.

Then Raoul heard Christine's voice. 'How can you talk like
that? When I sing only for you . . .? Tonight, I gave everything
to you, everything. And now I'm so tired.' Her voice was
unhappy and afraid.

Just then Raoul heard a man's voice in the room!

'You sang like an angel,' the man's voice said.

Raoul walked away. So that was the answer! Christine Daaé had a lover. But why was her voice so unhappy? He waited in the shadows near her room. He wanted to see her lover – his enemy!

After about ten minutes Christine came out of her room, alone, and walked away down the passage. Raoul waited, but no man came out after her. There was nobody in the passage, so Raoul went quickly up to the door of the dressing-room, opened it and went in. He closed the door quietly behind him, then called out:

'Where are you? I know you're in here! Come out!'

There was no answer. Raoul looked everywhere – under the chairs, behind all the clothes, in all the dark corners of the room. There was nobody there.

The Phantom is angry

That was Tuesday night. On Wednesday morning Monsieur Armand and Monsieur Firmin were happy men. Paris liked the new Margarita – everything in life was good. The next opera night was Friday. It was *Faust* again, but this time with La Carlotta singing Margarita.

By Wednesday afternoon they were not so happy. A second letter arrived for them – from O.G.

Why don't you listen to me? I am getting angry. Leave Box 5 free for me. And where are my 20,000 francs? On Friday Daaé must sing Margarita again. She is now the best singer in Paris. La Carlotta cannot sing – she has a very ugly voice, like a toad.

Remember, I am a bad enemy. O.G.

'So, Firmin, is this still a joke?' Monsieur Armand shouted. 'What are we going to do now, eh? Is O.G. the director here, or are we?'

'Don't shout, Armand,' said Monsieur Firmin tiredly. 'I don't know the answers. Let's talk to Madame Giry, the doorkeeper of Box 5. Perhaps she can help us.'

But Madame Giry was not helpful. Madame Giry was not afraid of ghosts, and she was not afraid of directors of Opera Houses.

'People say that you're a friend of the Opera ghost, Madame Giry,' Monsieur Armand began. 'Tell us about him. Some people say he has no head.'

'And some people say he has no body,' said Monsieur Firmin. 'What do *you* say, Madame Giry?'

Madame Giry looked at the two men and laughed. 'I say that the directors of the Opera House are fools!'

'What!' Monsieur Armand shouted. He stood up, and his face was red and angry. 'Listen to me, woman—'

'Oh, sit down, Armand, and listen,' said Monsieur Firmin. 'Why do you say that, Madame Giry?'

'Because, Monsieur, the Opera ghost is angry with you.

Madame Giry laughed. 'I say that the directors of the Opera House
are fools!'

When the ghost wants something, he must have it. He is clever
and dangerous, this ghost. The old directors before you, they
knew that, oh yes. At first they tried to stop him. Then there
were many accidents in the Opera House, many strange
accidents. And when did these accidents happen? When the
ghost was angry! So, the old directors learnt very quickly. The
ghost wants Box 5? He can have it every night. The ghost wants
money? Let's give the money to him at once. Oh yes, the old
directors understood very well.'

'But *we* are the directors, not the Opera ghost!' Monsieur
Armand shouted. He turned to Monsieur Firmin. 'This woman
is mad. Why do we listen to her? On Friday night La Carlotta
is going to sing Margarita. And you and I, Firmin, are going to
watch the opera from Box 5.'

'Well, we can try that, Armand. But we don't want any
accidents.'

Madame Giry came nearer to the two men. 'Listen to me,' she said quietly. 'Remember Joseph Buquet? I tell you, the Opera ghost is a good friend, but a bad enemy.'

The two men stared at her. 'Those words,' Monsieur Firmin said slowly, 'why did you say those words, Madame Giry?'

'Because the ghost says them to me. I never see him, but I often hear him. He has a very nice voice – and he doesn't shout at people.'

A letter for Raoul

That Wednesday a letter also arrived for the young Vicomte de Chagny. He opened the letter, saw the name at the bottom, and smiled for the first time that day.

> *Dear Raoul*
>
> *Of course I remember you! How could I forget you? Meet me on Thursday at three o'clock in the Tuileries Gardens. Don't be angry with me, Raoul, please.*
>
> *Christine Daaé*

Raoul put the letter carefully into his pocket. Angry? How could he be angry with an angel? On Thursday he was in the Tuileries Gardens by two o'clock.

At ten past three he began to feel unhappy. At half past three he wanted to die, or to kill somebody.

And then . . . she came. She ran through the gardens to him, and in a second she was in his arms.

'Oh, Christine!' he said, again and again. 'Oh Christine!' They walked through the gardens together and talked for a long time. They remembered their happy weeks in Brittany, four years ago.

'But why did you go away, Christine?' Raoul asked. 'Why didn't you write to me?'

For a minute or two Christine said nothing. Then she said slowly, 'We were so young, you and I. I was just a poor singer from Norway, and you . . . you were the Vicomte de Chagny. I knew I could never be your wife.'

'But I love you, Christine—'

'No, shh. Listen to me, Raoul, please. I went home to Norway, and a year later, my father died. I was very unhappy, but I came back to France, to Paris. I worked and worked at my singing, because I wanted to be an opera singer. Not just a good singer, but the best opera singer in Paris.'

'And now you are,' Raoul said. He smiled. 'All Paris is at your feet.'

Christine turned her face away and said nothing.

'Christine,' Raoul said quietly. 'I want to ask you a question. Who was the man in your dressing-room on Tuesday night? Tell me, please!'

Christine stopped and stared at him. Her face went white. 'What man?' she whispered. 'There was no man in my dressing-room on Tuesday night.'

Raoul put his hand on her arm. 'I heard him,' he said.

*Christine and Raoul walked through the gardens together
and talked for a long time.*

'I listened outside the door and heard a man's voice. Who was he?'

'Don't ask me, Raoul! There was a man's voice, yes, but there was no man in my room! It's true! Oh, Raoul, I'm so afraid. Sometimes I want to die.'

'Who is he? Tell me, Christine, please. I'm your friend, I can help you. Tell me his name!'

'I cannot tell you his name. It's a secret,' whispered Christine. 'I never see him, I only hear his voice. But he is everywhere! He sees everything, hears everything. That's why I didn't speak to you on Tuesday night. He is my music teacher, Raoul. He's a wonderful singer. I sang so well on Tuesday night because of him. I am famous because of him. He is my angel of music! And he says he loves me. How can I leave him?'

6

La Carlotta sings Margarita

On Friday morning La Carlotta had her breakfast in bed. She drank her coffee and opened her morning letters. One letter had no name on it. It was very short.

You are ill. You cannot sing Margarita tonight. Stay at home and don't go to the Opera House. Accidents can happen. Do you want to lose your voice – for ever?

La Carlotta opened her morning letters.

La Carlotta was very, very angry. She got out of bed at once and did not finish her breakfast.

'This is from Christine Daaé's friends,' she thought. 'They want her to sing again tonight. That Daaé girl is going to be sorry for this! I, La Carlotta, *I* am the best opera singer in Paris. And nothing is going to stop me singing Margarita tonight!'

At six o'clock that evening the dancers were in their dressing-room. They talked and laughed and put on their red and black dresses for *Faust*. But Meg Giry was very quiet.

'What's the matter, Meg?' Annie Sorelli asked.

'It's the Opera ghost,' Meg said. 'My mother says he's angry. She's afraid that something's going to happen tonight.'

'Oh, pooh!' the girl with black hair said. 'Who's afraid of an old ghost?'

An hour later Monsieur Armand and Monsieur Firmin went into Box 5 and sat down. They were not afraid of ghosts. Of course not. There were no ghosts in the Opera House.

Then Monsieur Armand saw some flowers on the floor by the door of the box. 'Firmin,' he whispered, 'did you put those flowers there?'

Monsieur Firmin looked. 'No, I didn't,' he whispered back. 'Did you?'

'Of course not, you fool! Shh, the music's beginning.'

La Carlotta did not sing for the first hour. There were no strange voices in Box 5, and the two directors began to feel happier. Then La Carlotta came out onto the stage, and Monsieur Firmin looked at Monsieur Armand.

'Did you hear a voice just then?' he asked quietly.

'No!' Monsieur Armand said, but he looked behind him twice, then three times, and suddenly felt cold.

La Carlotta sang and sang, and nothing happened. Then she began a beautiful love song.

'My love begins to – Co-ack!'

Everybody stared. What was the matter with Carlotta's voice? What was that strange noise – Co-ack?

Carlotta stopped and began the song again.

'My love begins to – Co-ack!

I cannot forget my – Co-ack!'

It was the noise of a toad! People began to talk and laugh. Monsieur Firmin put his head in his hands. Then he felt Monsieur Armand's hand on his arm. There was a voice in the box with them! A man's voice, laughing!

Poor Carlotta tried again, and again.

'I cannot forget my – Co-ack!'

Then the two directors heard the voice again, behind them, in front of them, everywhere. *'Her singing tonight is going to bring down the chandelier!'*

The two directors looked up at the top of the Opera House. Their faces were white. The famous chandelier, with its thousand lights, broke away from its ropes and crashed down on to the people below.

That was a terrible night for the Paris Opera House. One woman was killed by the chandelier, and many people were hurt. The Opera House closed for two weeks. And La Carlotta never sang again.

The famous chandelier broke away from its ropes and crashed down on to the people below.

7

My angel of music

For a week Raoul saw Christine every day. Some days Christine was quiet and unhappy, some days she laughed and sang. She never wanted to talk about the Opera House, or her singing, or Raoul's love for her. Raoul was very afraid for her. Who, or what, was this strange teacher, this man's voice, her 'angel of music'?

The tenth floor of the Opera House was a dangerous place.

Then one day there was no Christine. She was not at her home, not at the Opera House, not at their meeting places. Raoul looked everywhere and asked everybody. Where was Christine Daaé? But nobody knew.

Two days before the Opera House opened again, a letter arrived for Raoul. It was from Christine.

Meet me in an hour at the top of the Opera House, on the tenth floor.

The tenth floor of the Opera House was a dangerous place. There were hundreds of ropes going down to the stage below – it was a long, long way down.

Raoul and Christine sat in a dark corner, and Raoul took Christine's hands. Her face was white and tired.

'Listen, Raoul,' she said quietly. 'I'm going to tell you everything. But this is our last meeting. I can never see you again.'

'No, Christine!' Raoul cried. 'I love you, and we—'

'Shh! Quietly! Perhaps he can hear us. He's everywhere in the Opera House, Raoul!'

'Who? What are you talking about, Christine?'

'My angel of music. I couldn't meet you last Saturday because he came for me, and took me away. I was in my dressing-room in the Opera House and suddenly, he was there in front of me! I saw the voice for the first time! He wore black evening clothes and a mask over his face. He took me through many secret doors and passages, down, down under the Opera House. There is a lake down there, a big lake; the waters are black and cold. He took me across the lake in a boat to his house. He lives there, Raoul, in a house on the lake, under the Opera House!'

Raoul stared at her. Was his beautiful Christine mad? Christine saw his face, and said quickly:

'It's true, Raoul, it's true! And he . . . he is the Phantom of the Opera! But he's not a ghost, he's not an angel of music, he's a man! His name is Erik, and he loves me, he wants me to be his wife! No, Raoul, listen, there is more. He told me all this in his house, in a beautiful room. He said that no woman could ever love him, because of his face. He was so unhappy! Then he took off his mask, and I saw his face.'

She began to cry, and Raoul put his arms around her.

'Oh Raoul, he has the most terrible face! It is so ugly! I

'He took me across the lake in a boat to his house,' said Christine.

wanted to scream and run away. But where could I run to? He has the face of a dead man, Raoul, but he is not dead! He has no nose, just two black holes in his yellow face. And his eyes! Sometimes they are black holes, sometimes they have a terrible red light . . .'

She put her face in her hands for a second. Then she said, 'I stayed in his house for five days. He was very good to me, and I felt sorry for him, Raoul. He wants me to love him, and I told him . . . I told him . . .'

'No, Christine, no! You're going to be *my* wife! Come away with me at once, today! You can't go back to him.'

'But I must,' Christine said quietly. 'He knows about you, Raoul. He knows about us. He says he's going to kill you. I must go back to him.'

'Never!' said Raoul. 'I love you, Christine, and I'm going to kill this Erik!'

Erik ... Erik ... Erik ... Erik ... The word whispered round the Opera House. Raoul and Christine stared.

'What was that?' Raoul said, afraid. 'Was that ... *his* voice? Where did it come from?'

'I'm afraid, Raoul,' Christine whispered. 'I'm singing Margarita again on Saturday. What's going to happen?'

'This,' Raoul said. 'After the opera on Saturday night, you and I are going away together. Come on, let's go down now. I don't like it up here.'

They went carefully along a dark passage to some stairs, then suddenly stopped. There was a man in front of them, a tall man in a long dark coat and a black hat. He turned and looked at them.

'No, not these stairs,' he said. 'Go to the stairs at the front. And go quickly!'

Christine turned and ran. Raoul ran after her.

'Who was that man?' he asked.

'It's the Persian,' Christine answered.

'But who is he? What's his name? Why did he tell us to go to the front stairs?'

'Nobody knows his name. He's just the Persian. He's always in the Opera House. I think he knows about Erik, but he never talks about him. Perhaps he saw Erik on those stairs, and wanted to help us.'

Hand in hand, they ran quickly down the stairs, through passages, then more stairs and more passages. At one of the

'No, *not these stairs*,' the man said. 'Go to the stairs at the front.
And go quickly!'

little back doors to the Opera House, they stopped.

'On Saturday night, then. After the opera,' Raoul said. 'I'm going to take you away, and marry you.'

Christine looked up into his face. 'Yes, Raoul.'

Then they kissed, there by the door of the Opera House. Their first kiss.

8

Where is Christine Daaé?

On Saturday morning Comte Philippe looked across the breakfast table at his brother.

'Don't do it, Raoul, please. All this talk about ghosts and phantoms. I think the girl is mad.'

'She's not mad, and I'm going to marry her,' Raoul said.

'She's only a little opera singer,' Philippe said unhappily. 'And she's very young. Are you still going to love her in ten, or twenty, years' time?'

Raoul drank his coffee and did not answer.

There were two more unhappy faces in the Opera House, too. The directors now understood about O.G. They didn't want any more accidents.

'Box 5 is free tonight for O.G. Daaé is singing Margarita. And here is 20,000 francs. Madame Giry can leave the money in Box 5 for him. Is that everything?' Monsieur Armand asked Monsieur Firmin.

'It's a lot of money,' Monsieur Firmin said unhappily. He thought for a minute. 'What about some flowers in Box 5? Madame Giry says that O.G. likes flowers.'

'O.G. can bring his own flowers!' shouted Monsieur Armand.

The evening began well. The chandelier was now back in place, with new ropes. All Paris was in the Opera House. Everybody wanted to hear Christine Daaé's voice again. People also knew about the love story between Christine Daaé and the Vicomte de Chagny. There are no love secrets in Paris! People watched the Comte and the Vicomte in Box 14 with interest. Young men from families like de Chagny do not marry opera singers.

People watched the Comte and the Vicomte in Box 14 with interest.

When Christine came on to the stage, her face was white and she looked afraid. But she sang like an angel. Ah, what a voice! All Paris was in love with Christine Daaé.

She began to sing the famous love song. Suddenly, every light in the Opera House went out. For a second nobody moved or spoke. Then a woman screamed, and all the lights came on again.

But Christine Daaé was no longer on the stage! She was not behind the stage, she was not under the stage. Nobody could find her.

The Opera House went mad. Everybody ran here and there, shouted and called. In the directors' office, people ran in and out. The police came, and asked questions. But nobody could answer the questions. Monsieur Armand got angry and shouted, and Monsieur Firmin told him to be quiet. Then Madame Giry arrived in the office with her daughter Meg.

'Go away, woman!' Monsieur Armand shouted.

'Monsieur, there are three people missing now!' Madame Giry said. 'Meg, tell the directors your story.'

This was Meg's story.

'When the lights went out, we were just behind the stage. We heard a scream – I think it was Christine Daaé's voice. Then the lights came back on, but Christine wasn't there! We were very afraid, and we began to run back to our dressing-room. There were people running everywhere! Then we saw the Vicomte de Chagny. His face was red and he was very angry. "Where's Christine? Where's Christine?" he shouted. Suddenly the Persian came up behind him and took his arm. He said

'Meg, tell the directors your story,' said Madame Giry.

something to the Vicomte and they went into Christine Daaé's dressing-room . . .'

'Yes? And then?' Monsieur Firmin said quickly. 'What happened next?'

'Nobody knows!' Meg's face was white. 'We looked into Christine Daaé's dressing-room, but . . . but there was nobody there!'

9

The house on the lake

When the lights came on, Raoul ran. He ran down stairs and along passages, through the Opera House to the back of the stage. In the passage outside Christine's dressing-room, a hand took his arm.

'What's the matter, my young friend? Where are you running to, so quickly?'

Raoul turned and saw the long face of the Persian under his black hat.

'Christine!' Raoul said quickly. 'Erik's got her. Where is she? Help me! How do I get to his house on the lake?'

'Come with me,' said the Persian. They went quickly into Christine's dressing-room. The Persian closed the door and went to the big mirror on one wall.

'There's only one door into this room,' Raoul began.

'Wait,' the Persian said. He put his hands on the big mirror, first here, then there. For a minute nothing happened. Then the mirror began to move and turn, and a big dark hole opened in it. Raoul stared.

'Quick! Come with me, but be careful,' the Persian said. 'I know Erik. I understand his secrets. Put your right hand up near your head, like this, and keep it there all the time.'

'But why?' Raoul asked.

'Remember Joseph Buquet, and the rope around his neck? Erik is a clever man with ropes in the dark.'

The mirror began to move and turn, and a big dark hole opened in it.

They went down, down, down, under the Opera House. They went through secret doors in the floors, then along passages and down dark stairs. The Persian listened carefully all the time for strange noises.

'When do we get to the lake?' Raoul whispered.

'We're not going by the lake. Erik watches it all the time. No, we go round the lake and get into Erik's house from the back. I know some secret doors.'

Soon they were there. In the dark, the Persian felt the wall carefully with his hands. 'Ah, here it is,' he whispered. The wall moved under his hands and a small door opened. Very quietly, they went through, and then the door closed behind them. They could not get out.

Inside the room it was very dark. They waited and listened. The Persian put his hands on the wall.

'Oh no!' he whispered. 'It was the wrong door! This is Erik's torture room – the room of mirrors! We are dead men, Vicomte de Chagny, dead men!'

At first Raoul did not understand. But he soon learnt. The lights came on, and they heard a man's laugh. Erik knew they were there.

The room was all mirrors – walls, floor, ceiling. There were pictures in the mirrors of trees and flowers and rivers. The pictures moved and danced in front of their eyes. And the room was hot. It got hotter and hotter and hotter. Raoul was thirsty, hot and thirsty, and the rivers in the pictures danced and laughed at him. He closed his eyes, but the rivers still danced. Water, he needed water, but the mirrors laughed at him. Soon

The pictures moved and danced in front of their eyes.

he could not move or speak, or open his eyes. He was not thirsty now, just tired, so tired. 'Oh Christine, I'm sorry,' he thought. 'I wanted to help you, and now I'm dying . . .'

Through a mirror in the wall Christine watched her lover in the torture room. Behind her Erik stood, with his hands on her arms.

'He's dying, Christine, dying. Watch him carefully. No, don't close your eyes. Watch him!'

Christine could not speak. She wanted to scream, but no words came. Then she found her voice again.

'How can you do this, Erik! Why don't you kill me?'

'Because I love you, Christine. Marry me, be my wife, and love me. Then Raoul and the Persian can live.'

'*From this minute I am your wife,*' *said Christine, very slowly.*

Slowly, Christine turned. She looked into Erik's terrible, ugly face, and spoke again, very quietly.

'Yes, Erik. From this minute I am your wife.' She put her arms around Erik's neck, and kissed him – kissed him slowly and lovingly on his ugly mouth. Then she took her arms away and said slowly, 'Poor, unhappy Erik.'

Erik stared at her. 'You kissed me!' he whispered. 'I didn't ask you, but you kissed me – freely! Oh Christine, my angel! That was my first kiss from a woman. Even my mother never kissed me! She gave me my first mask when I was two years old. She turned her face away from me every time I came near her.'

Erik put his ugly face in his hands and cried. Then he went down on the floor at Christine's feet. 'You are free, Christine, free! Go away and marry your Raoul, and be happy. But remember Erik, sometimes. Go now, quickly! Take Raoul and the Persian, and go!'

Madame Giry visits the Persian

For weeks, all Paris talked about that night at the opera. Everybody asked questions, but nobody knew the answers. Where was Christine Daaé? Where was the Vicomte de Chagny? Were they alive, or dead?

And the Phantom of the Opera . . .?

Some weeks after that famous night Madame Giry went out

one afternoon to a small house near the Rivoli Gardens. She went in and up the stairs to some rooms at the top of the house. The Persian opened the door.

Madame Giry looked at him. 'My friend, you know the answers. Please tell me. Are they alive or dead?'

'Come in,' the Persian said quietly.

They sat down on some chairs by the window, and looked out across the Rivoli Gardens.

'Yes,' the Persian said slowly, 'The Phantom is dead now. He did not want to live any longer. I saw his body three days ago, and because of that, I can talk to you about him. He cannot kill me now.'

'So the Phantom was really a man?' Madame Giry asked.

'Yes, his name was Erik. That was not his real name, of course. He was born in France, but I knew him in Persia. He was a famous builder and I worked with him there. For a time I was his friend, but not for long. When he came to Paris, I came after him – I wanted to watch him. He was a very clever, very dangerous man. He could be in two, or three, places at the same time. He could be in one place, and his voice could come from another place. He could do many clever things with ropes, and mirrors, and secret doors. You see, he helped to build the Opera House. He built secret passages underground, and his secret house on the lake. He could not live in the outside world, because of his terrible, ugly face. Unhappy Erik! We can feel sorry for him, Madame Giry. He was so clever . . . and so ugly. People screamed when they saw his face. And so he lived this strange life – half-man, half-phantom. But he was a man,

'*Unhappy Erik! He was so clever . . . and so ugly.
People screamed when they saw his face.*'

in the end. He wanted a woman's love . . .'

He stopped, and Madame Giry asked quietly, 'And Christine Daaé and Vicomte Raoul? What happened to them?'

The Persian smiled. 'Ah yes! What happened to young Raoul and the beautiful Christine . . .? Who knows?'

Nobody in Paris ever saw Raoul and Christine again. Perhaps they took a train to the north, and lived a quiet, happy life together there. Perhaps Christine's wonderful voice is still singing, somewhere in the cold and beautiful mountains of Norway. Who knows?

GLOSSARY

alone   not with other people

angel   a messenger from God, or a very special, wonderful
person

box   a small 'room' with three walls in a theatre; you can
watch the stage from a box, but other people can't see you

chandelier   a very big, beautiful light, which has lots of little
lights in it

clever   quick to understand and learn

crash *(v)*   to fall or hit something hard and noisily

dancer   someone who dances (moving the body to music)

dangerous   something dangerous can hurt or kill you

director   somebody who is the head person in a company,
theatre, etc.

doorkeeper   (in this story) a person who looks after the boxes
in a theatre

enemy   the opposite of a friend

floor   all the rooms on the same level in a building

fool   someone who is stupid, not quick at understanding or
learning

ghost   people can see the ghost of a dead person

ground   the ground is under our feet

hole   a small opening in something

joke   something people say or do to make other people laugh

kiss   to touch someone lovingly with your mouth

lake   a big area of water, with land all round it

light *(n)*   to see in the dark, you need a light

mad   ill in the head

mask   a cover that you put over the face to hide it

mirror   a piece of glass where you can see yourself (some
special mirrors you can also look through, like a window)

missing *(adj)*   if something or someone is missing, you can't find them

music   when you sing or play an instrument, you make music

neck   the part of the body between the head and the shoulders

opera   a play in a theatre which has singing and music

passage   a long narrow place in a building between rooms

phantom   a ghost

rope   very thick, strong string

scream   to cry out in a very loud, high voice

secret   something that you do not tell other people

shadow   a place or thing that is dark because there is something between it and the light

shout   to speak or cry very loudly and strongly

stage   the part of a theatre where actors, singers, and dancers stand and move

stare   to look at someone or something for a long time

terrible   very, very bad

toad   a small animal, like a frog, that lives in wet places

torture *(n)*   doing very painful, terrible things to people's bodies

ugly   not beautiful

voice   you talk or sing with your voice

whisper   to speak very, very quietly

The Phantom of the Opera

ACTIVITIES

ACTIVITIES

Before Reading

Read the story introduction on the first page of the book,
and the back cover. How much do you know now about the
Phantom of the Opera?
Tick one box for each sentence.

	YES	NO
1 He is a body with two heads.	☐	☐
2 He has the head of a dead man.	☐	☐
3 He has a white face.	☐	☐
4 He wears a red evening coat.	☐	☐
5 He has black holes for eyes.	☐	☐
6 He has a very big nose.	☐	☐
7 He lives in a house next to the Opera House.	☐	☐
8 Everybody is afraid of him.	☐	☐

2 **What is going to happen in the story? Can you guess? Tick
one box for each sentence.**

	YES	NO	PERHAPS
1 The Phantom goes away and nobody sees him again.	☐	☐	☐
2 Somebody kills the Phantom.	☐	☐	☐
3 The Phantom kills somebody.	☐	☐	☐
4 The Phantom marries an opera singer.	☐	☐	☐
5 The Opera House closes and never opens again.	☐	☐	☐

ACTIVITIES

While Reading

Read Chapters 1 and 2, then answer these questions.

Who

1 . . . did Annie Sorelli see in the passage?
2 . . . sometimes found flowers in Box 5?
3 . . . was dead, with a rope around his neck?
4 . . . was very angry about a letter?
5 . . . was a good friend, but a bad enemy?
6 . . . could not sing in the opera that night?

Read Chapters 3 and 4. Here are some untrue sentences about them. Change them into true sentences.

1 Christine Daaé sang very badly that night.
2 Philippe de Chagny was in love with Christine Daaé.
3 Raoul heard a child's voice in Christine's room.
4 The two directors were very happy about the second letter from O.G.
5 O.G. wanted La Carlotta to sing on Friday night.
6 Madame Giry never heard the ghost, but she often saw him.

Read Chapters 5 and 6. Who said or wrote this?

1 'Of course I remember you! How could I forget you?'
2 'I'm your friend, I can help you.'
3 'Accidents can happen.'
4 'Nothing is going to stop me singing Margarita tonight!'
5 'Did you put those flowers there?'
6 'Her singing tonight is going to bring down the chandelier!'

Read Chapters 7 and 8. Choose the best question-word for these questions, and then answer them.

Who / Where

1 . . . was Christine's 'angel of music'?
2 . . . did the Phantom live?
3 . . . told Christine and Raoul to go to the front stairs?
4 . . . thought Christine was mad?
5 . . . did Raoul and the Persian go?
6 . . . did the dancers see when they looked in the room?

Before you read Chapters 9 and 10, can you guess the answers to these questions?

1 Where is Christine Daaé?
2 Do Raoul and the Persian find her?
3 What does Erik do?
4 Does Raoul marry Christine in the end?

48

ACTIVITIES

After Reading

1 Before the Phantom died, perhaps he left a letter for the Persian. Use these words from the story to complete the letter. (Use each word once.)

because, enemies, face, free, friend, good, happy, kissed, love, scream, sorry, terrible, ugly, unhappy, when, without, woman, wonderful

To the Persian

I am leaving this letter for you, because once you were my _____. Now, of course, I have only _____. People _____ when they see my _____. I am clever, it is true, but no _____ can ever love me. And how can a man live without _____?

When I was a child, I was very _____. My mother never _____ me. She didn't want to look at me _____ I was so _____. And years later, _____ I was a man, I did many _____ things. I know that, and I am _____ now. But I did one _____ thing in my life. Christine is _____. She can marry the Vicomte and be _____.

But I can never forget her _____ voice, and I cannot live _____ her.

And so, goodbye.

Erik

2 **Here is a new illustration for the story. Find the best place in the story to put the picture, and answer these questions.**

The picture goes on page _____.

1 Who are the characters in this picture?
2 What can they hear behind them?
3 What is happening on the stage at this time?

Now write a caption for the illustration.

Caption: _____

3 Here is a conversation between Meg Giry and her mother. It happened on Friday morning (see page 19). The conversation is in the wrong order. Write it out in the correct order and put in the speakers' names. Meg speaks first (number 7).

1 _____ 'Oh, dear! What's he angry about?'

2 _____ 'I told them two days ago, but they didn't listen to me. I'm afraid, Meg.'

3 _____ 'What about him?'

4 _____ 'I don't know, Meg, I don't know. But the ghost is clever – and dangerous. I think something terrible is going to happen tonight.'

5 _____ 'No, I'm not happy, Meg. It's the Opera ghost.'

6 _____ 'La Carlotta is singing Margarita tonight, but the ghost wants Christine Daaé to sing. And when the ghost wants something, he must have it.'

7 _____ 'What's the matter, Mama? You don't look very happy.'

8 _____ 'You must tell the directors. They can change the singer for tonight.'

9 _____ 'But why, Mama? What are you afraid of?'

10 _____ 'I heard his voice this morning, in Box 5. He's very angry.'

4 **Here is a different ending for the story, after Chapter 9. Fill in the gaps (you can use as many words as you want).**

Just then _____ broke down the door of the room of mirrors, and _____. Erik looked at Raoul. 'You _____,' he said quietly. 'Take _____!'

Raoul ran to Christine, but she _____ and took _____ hand. 'No, Raoul,' she said. 'Erik _____, and I _____.'

So Christine _____, and _____ in the house on the lake. Raoul _____.

5 **What really happens at the end of the story? The Persian doesn't tell us, but here is another ending. Which of the two different endings on this page do you like best, and why?**

Christine and Raoul left the Opera House, and they married the next day. They went to Norway and lived there happily for many years, but Christine never sang in an opera house again. Raoul's brother, Philippe, often visited them, and he and Christine were good friends.

ABOUT THE AUTHOR

Jennifer Bassett has worked in English Language Teaching since 1972. She has been a teacher, teacher trainer, editor, and materials writer, and has taught in England, Greece, Spain and Portugal. She is the current Series Editor of the Oxford Bookworms Library, and has written several other stories for the series, including *One-Way Ticket* and *The President's Murderer* (both at Stage 1). She lives and works in Devonshire, in the south-west of England.

For this story about the Phantom of the Opera, she used many sources. The first story was written by a Frenchman, Gaston Leroux, in 1911. His book was very popular, and in 1925 it was made into an American silent film, with the great Lon Chaney as the Phantom. Since then, there have been many other films and plays, and, most recently, the famous British musical by Andrew Lloyd Webber. Every time the story is retold, it changes a little, and sometimes has a different ending.

OXFORD BOOKWORMS LIBRARY

Classics • Crime & Mystery • Factfiles • Fantasy & Horror
Human Interest • Playscripts • Thriller & Adventure
True Stories • World Stories

The OXFORD BOOKWORMS LIBRARY provides enjoyable reading in English, with a wide range of classic and modern fiction, non-fiction, and plays. It includes original and adapted texts in seven carefully graded language stages, which take learners from beginner to advanced level. An overview is given on the next pages.

All Stage 1 titles are available as audio recordings, as well as over eighty other titles from Starter to Stage 6. All Starters and many titles at Stages 1 to 4 are specially recommended for younger learners. Every Bookworm is illustrated, and Starters and Factfiles have full-colour illustrations.

The OXFORD BOOKWORMS LIBRARY also offers extensive support. Each book contains an introduction to the story, notes about the author, a glossary, and activities. Additional resources include tests and worksheets, and answers for these and for the activities in the books. There is advice on running a class library, using audio recordings, and the many ways of using Oxford Bookworms in reading programmes. Resource materials are available on the website <www.oup.com/bookworms>.

The *Oxford Bookworms Collection* is a series for advanced learners. It consists of volumes of short stories by well-known authors, both classic and modern. Texts are not abridged or adapted in any way, but carefully selected to be accessible to the advanced student.

You can find details and a full list of titles in the *Oxford Bookworms Library Catalogue* and *Oxford English Language Teaching Catalogues*, and on the website <www.oup.com/bookworms>.

THE OXFORD BOOKWORMS LIBRARY
GRADING AND SAMPLE EXTRACTS

STARTER • 250 HEADWORDS

present simple – present continuous – imperative –
can/cannot, *must* – *going to* (future) – simple gerunds …

Her phone is ringing – but where is it?

Sally gets out of bed and looks in her bag. No phone. She looks under the bed. No phone. Then she looks behind the door. There is her phone. Sally picks up her phone and answers it. *Sally's Phone*

STAGE 1 • 400 HEADWORDS

… past simple – coordination with *and, but, or* – subordination with *before, after, when, because, so* …

I knew him in Persia. He was a famous builder and I worked with him there. For a time I was his friend, but not for long. When he came to Paris, I came after him – I wanted to watch him. He was a very clever, very dangerous man. *The Phantom of the Opera*

STAGE 2 • 700 HEADWORDS

… present perfect – *will* (future) – *(don't) have to, must not, could* – comparison of adjectives – simple *if* clauses – past continuous – tag questions – *ask/tell* + infinitive …

While I was writing these words in my diary, I decided what to do. I must try to escape. I shall try to get down the wall outside. The window is high above the ground, but I have to try. I shall take some of the gold with me – if I escape, perhaps it will be helpful later. *Dracula*

STAGE 3 • 1000 HEADWORDS

… should, may – present perfect continuous – *used to* – past perfect –
causative – relative clauses – indirect statements …

Of course, it was most important that no one should see
Colin, Mary, or Dickon entering the secret garden. So Colin
gave orders to the gardeners that they must all keep away
from that part of the garden in future. *The Secret Garden*

STAGE 4 • 1400 HEADWORDS

… past perfect continuous – passive (simple forms) –
would conditional clauses – indirect questions –
relatives with *where/when* – gerunds after prepositions/phrases …

I was glad. Now Hyde could not show his face to the world
again. If he did, every honest man in London would be
proud to report him to the police. *Dr Jekyll and Mr Hyde*

STAGE 5 • 1800 HEADWORDS

… future continuous – future perfect –
passive (modals, continuous forms) –
would have conditional clauses – modals + perfect infinitive …

If he had spoken Estella's name, I would have hit him. I was
so angry with him, and so depressed about my future, that I
could not eat the breakfast. Instead I went straight to the old
house. *Great Expectations*

STAGE 6 • 2500 HEADWORDS

… passive (infinitives, gerunds) – advanced modal meanings –
clauses of concession, condition

When I stepped up to the piano, I was confident. It was as if I
knew that the prodigy side of me really did exist. And when
I started to play, I was so caught up in how lovely I looked
that I didn't worry how I would sound. *The Joy Luck Club*

BOOKWORMS • FANTASY & HORROR • STAGE 1

The Monkey's Paw

W. W. JACOBS

Retold by Diane Mowat

Outside, the night is cold and wet. Inside, the White family sits and waits. Where is their visitor?

There is a knock at the door. A man is standing outside in the dark. Their visitor has arrived.

The visitor waits. He has been in India for many years. What has he got? He has brought the hand of a small, dead animal – a monkey's paw.

Outside, in the dark, the visitor smiles and waits for the door to open.

BOOKWORMS • CRIME & MYSTERY • STAGE 1

Sister Love and Other Crime Stories

JOHN ESCOTT

Some sisters are good friends, some are not. Sometimes there is more hate in a family than there is love. Karin is beautiful and has lots of men friends, but she can be very unkind to her sister Marcia. Perhaps when they were small, there was love between them, but that was a long time ago.

They say that everybody has one crime in them. Perhaps they only take an umbrella that does not belong to them. Perhaps they steal from a shop, perhaps they get angry and hit someone, perhaps they kill . . .